CONTENTS

Contributors:
Charley Darbishire
Simon Little
Andy Park
Glenn Rogers
Claire Thompson
Chrissy Williams

Consultant:
Maf Gibbons

Published by Coordination Group Publications Ltd
ISBN 1 84146 456 2
Groovy website: www.cgpbooks.co.uk

Printed by Elanders Hindson, Newcastle upon Tyne.
Clipart sources: CorelDRAW and VECTOR.
With thanks to Microsoft for permission to use screenshots from MS Powerpoint,
MS Excel and MS Internet Explorer and thanks to KITE for permission to use Flowol.
Text, design, layout and original illustrations © Coordination Group Publications Ltd
All rights reserved.

Multimedia Software

Multimedia software can do loads of things. It can play sounds and music, show videos, pictures and animations, and do a zillion other cool things.

Multimedia Software can do Loads of Stuff

Loads of CD-ROMs and Internet pages use multimedia. They sometimes look a bit like the screen below, with buttons on the page that do cool things when you click on them.

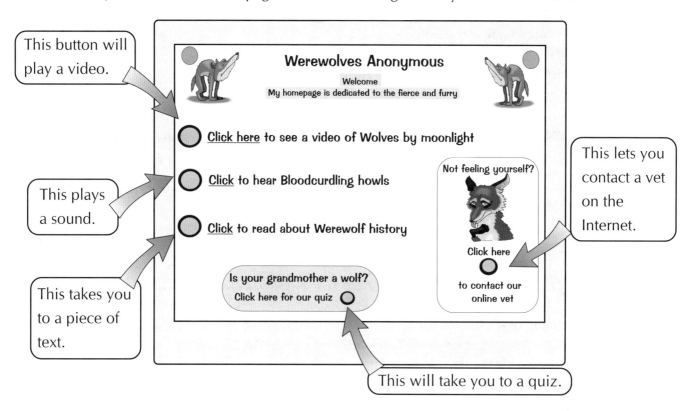

- ✸ Multimedia pages are often interactive — you control what happens by clicking on the buttons.

- ✸ Examples of multimedia software are: web design software (where you make web pages), presentation software (where you make a 'slide show'), some word processors and spreadsheets.

Multimedia has Good and Bad Points

Some Advantages of using Multimedia:	Some Disadvantages of using Multimedia:
1. It's fun.	1. It's not always easy to carry computers around with you.
2. It's really easy to use.	2. Computers are really expensive.
3. It's interactive.	3. Computers sometimes crash
4. It can be quicker than using a book.	— books don't.

Multimedia Software

① Name 3 things a multimedia page can do.

1. ....

2. ....

3. ....

② Multimedia has advantages and disadvantages.

Give one advantage and one disadvantage of multimedia.

Advantage: ....

....

Disadvantage: ....

....

This one'll think
twice before using
a CD-ROM again.
Heh, heh, heh...

③ Use the words to complete these sentences.

choose

button

multimedia

interactive

buttons

Multimedia pages often have ....

that you click on. Each .... usually

does something different. A ....

page is often .... — that

means the reader can .... what to

look at.

Page Design

When you're making a web page or a slide, it's really important to make your page easy to use.

Think Carefully about Good Design

You have to think carefully about where to put things. These two pages use the same information, but they've been designed really differently.

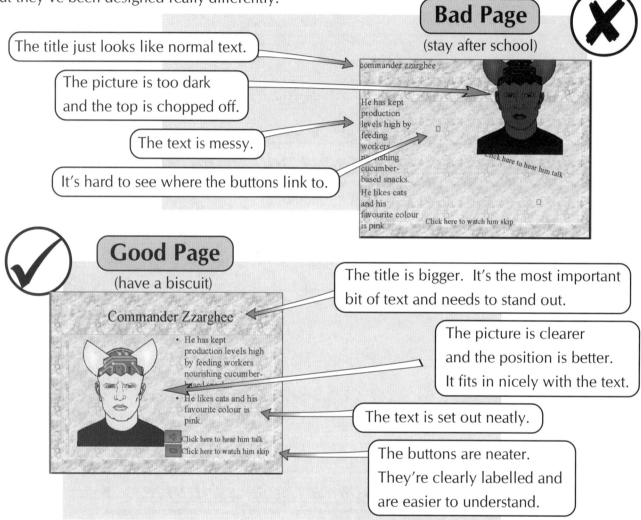

Bad Page
(stay after school)

The title just looks like normal text.

The picture is too dark and the top is chopped off.

The text is messy.

It's hard to see where the buttons link to.

Good Page
(have a biscuit)

The title is bigger. It's the most important bit of text and needs to stand out.

The picture is clearer and the position is better. It fits in nicely with the text.

The text is set out neatly.

The buttons are neater. They're clearly labelled and are easier to understand.

Planning how to use the space is just as important as making everything look pretty.

Keep it Simple

The basic rule is to keep your page looking neat and tidy at all times — that way no one gets hurt. These are the things to remember if you want everyone to be dead jealous of your page:

1. **Title** — Is it big enough?

2. **Pictures** — Are they bright and clear enough?

3. **Text** — Is it easy to read?

4. **Buttons** — Is it easy to understand what they do?

If you try to cram too much in, then your page will just look really squashed and everyone will say you smell.

Page Design

① What's wrong with this multimedia page?

Write down **four** things that could be improved on this page.

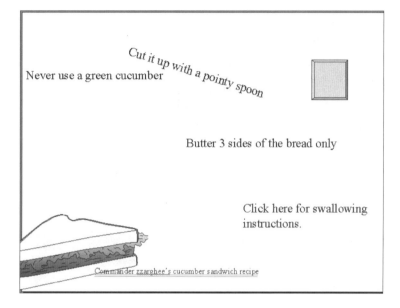

1. ....

2. ....

3. ....

4. ....

② Which of these is the most important?

Tick the thing that's important to remember when making a multimedia page.

Thinking about where to put things ☐   Thinking about the meaning of life ☐

FIND SOME REALLY BAD WEB PAGES...

Find a homepage on the **Internet** which you think is **badly designed**. Then find a page which you think is **well designed**. Print out each page. Now **mark** on each page the bits which you think **work well** and the bits which work **badly**.

Recording Sounds

You can record sounds for your multimedia pages using the Windows **Sound Recorder**.

Windows has its own Sound Recorder

This is how to find the Sound Recorder (although your menus might look a little bit different).

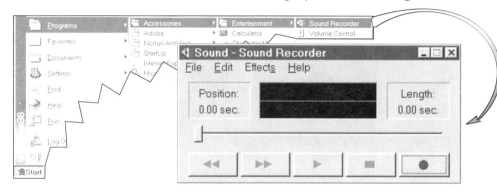

The Volume Control is usually on the same menu.

Recording Sounds is Easy

(1) Click here to **record**.

(2) Click here to **stop** recording.

(3) Click here to **play** it back.

Saving your Sounds is just as Simple

You can save your recording as a sound file.

1. Click on "Save As" in the File Menu.

2. Give your file a name.

3. Click on "Save".

To **play your sound file** again you can use Windows Explorer — double-clicking on the icon will play your recorded sound.

Chrissy giggling 27KB

Mike's been a bit quiet lately...

Why isn't this microphone working? I demand to see the manager.

If you're having trouble recording something, check the microphone volume isn't set to "Mute". Do this on the Volume Control menu.

Recording Sounds

① Label these buttons on the sound recorder.

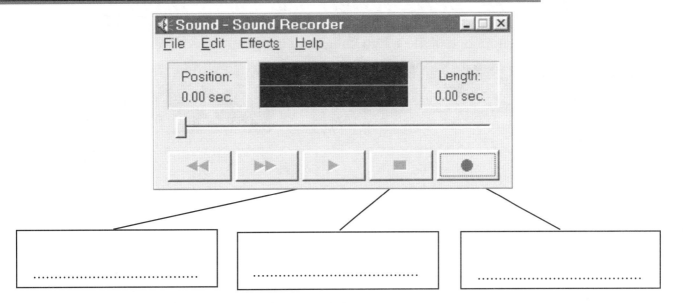

....	....	....

② Use the words to complete these sentences.

You can .... your recording as a

....

To play your sound you can

.... on it

in Windows ....

save

Explorer

sound file

double-click

③ Which of these should you try if it doesn't work?

Circle the one you think is the right answer, like this: (D)

A — Throwing the microphone out of the window.

Tonight, ladies and gentlemen, I'd like to start with a number I wrote myself entitled "Too many crackers can keep a good parrot down"...

B — Checking the microphone isn't set to mute.

C — Speaking in a louder voice.

D — Kicking the parrot.

Buttons

Buttons, Hotspots and Hyperlinks are the same thing — you click on them and something happens.

Something Happens when you Click a Button

When you click on a button, one of these two things will happen:

 The computer might open a new file (e.g. a sound file or a picture file).

 You might jump to a different part of the same file (e.g. the next page of a document or slide show).

Open a sound file, (i.e. play a sound).

Open a picture file (i.e. show a picture).

Jump to the next page of the document.

Jump to the homepage.

> A homepage is the 'first page' of a website — it says what the site is about, and usually has lots of links to other pages.

Draw a Button — then Link it to Something

To make a button you have to do these **two** things:

 Type a word, or draw a picture or a shape — this will be your button.

 Select your button, and link it to a new file (or a different part of the same file) — you might need to click on a hyperlink button for this.

You'll see a menu something like this one — this is where you say what you want to link to.

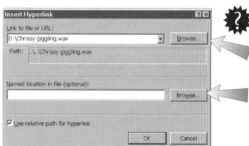

You have to choose...

 Either: Click here to link to a different file.

 Or: Click here to link to a different part of the same file.

> Your menu might look different to this one, but all you're doing is choosing what to link to.

Bet you thought that was going to be complicated...

Yeah, well it isn't — it's a piece of cake. Make a button then link it to something. No problem.

Buttons

① Write down two other names for a button.

1. ....

2. ....

② What can happen when you click on a button?

Tick the things that could happen when you click on a button.

☐ Your computer could catch fire.

☐ The computer could open a new file.

☐ You could jump to a different part of the same document.

☐ A small dog called Pete could appear and bite your big toe.

③ What is a website's homepage?

....

....

MAKE A PAGE OF SOUNDS

Now try creating a **page of sounds** in your multimedia program.
First, decide **what kind** of page it's going to be.

It could be • a page of **musical instrument** sounds
             • a musical **birthday greeting**
             • a page of **animal noises**

You can either **record** the sounds yourself or **copy** sounds from a CD-ROM.
Your page should use **buttons** to activate the sounds and use a nice layout.

Linking Pages

Buttons can also link different 'pages' together. 'Pages' could be completely different documents, or different parts of the same document — it depends on what software you're using.

Draw a 'Map' to Plan your Links

Before you start linking pages willy-nilly, it's good to draw a 'map' to show all the links you need.

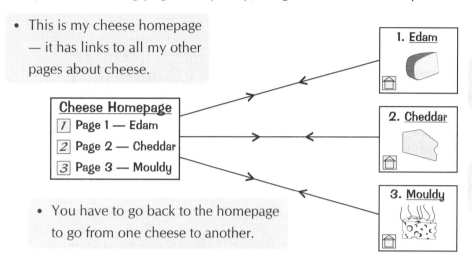

- This is my cheese homepage — it has links to all my other pages about cheese.

- You have to go back to the homepage to go from one cheese to another.

- Each page has a link back to the homepage.

- The homepage button looks like a home —

I've got my map — now I can make all my cheese pages. I'm really looking forward to it.

Make it Clear what the Buttons Do

I've made my cheese site. And I've also added some more links — now you can read pages 1 to 3 without going to the homepage.

The buttons are easy to understand

This is because they:

   a. look the same on each page,

   b. are in the same place on every page (and are easy to find),

   c. are clearly labelled.

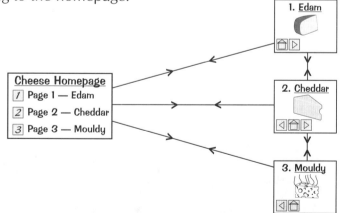

Linking pages pun...

Making a site like this is easy...

1) First you draw a 'map' of your website or slide show.
2) Then you make all your pages.
3) And when you've done all that, you can link the pages together like on your map.

Linking Pages

① Why is it good to link your pages together?

Tick the boxes next to the right answers (there can be more than one).

A. It's easy to go straight to what you want.

C. It will make you more popular.

B. It's a quick way to jump between pages.

D. The pages won't get lonely.

② Draw the links between these pages.

Look at the buttons on these pages, and then add the links to this map.

Make sure you mark arrows on your links to show which way you can jump between pages.

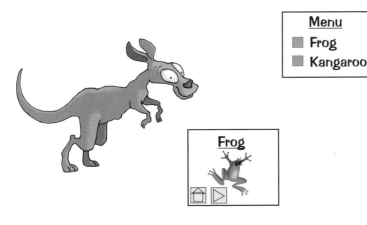

③ List 3 ways to keep your buttons easy to understand.

1. ....

2. ....

3. ....

④ What does the HYPERLINK BUTTON look like?

a)

b)

c)

d)

Telling a Story

You can 'tell' an interactive story using different pages and some carefully planned buttons.

Buttons can Help you Tell a Story

An interactive story is when the reader chooses what happens next.

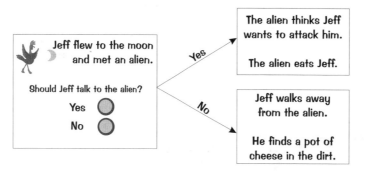

This map shows what the reader will see on screen — each box will be a different page.

Plan each Page on Paper First

You need to plan each stage of the story on paper first — so make a map like this.

Number each page so you don't get muddled.

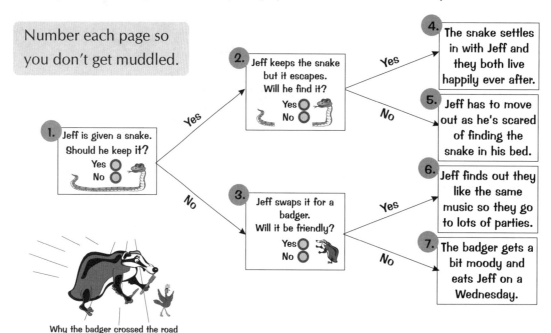

Why the badger crossed the road

Plan your pages or the chicken gets it...

The most important thing is to sort out where everything goes on paper before you start using the computer. You're just less likely to get all confused that way. Trust me.

Telling a Story

① What does 'interactive' mean?

A. The reader chooses what happens next.

B. The reader likes sports.

C. The chicken gets it.

② What's the first thing you should do?

What's the first thing you need to do when you want to write an interactive story?

A. Plan it all on paper first.

B. Choose what colour buttons you want to use.

C. Decide who will eat the main character.

③ Fill in the gaps in the diagram below.

Complete the plan for this interactive story — show what choices the reader will have.

(If you get stuck, use the map at the top of page 12 as a guide.)

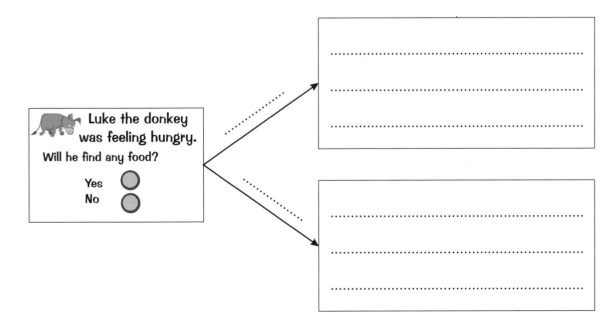

Computer Activity

Tell a Story

For this activity you'll need software that can link between different 'pages'. This could include MS Powerpoint, MS Excel, or MS Word, but there's plenty of different software you could use.

In this activity you will:

Design pages and make them into an interactive story

Planning the story:

 Start off by making up something you want to tell a story about, (e.g. a giraffe called Lionel or a buffalo named Pink).

 Draw a map on paper to show how the story will go — use boxes and arrows. (You could copy the shape of the one below, but add your own ideas)

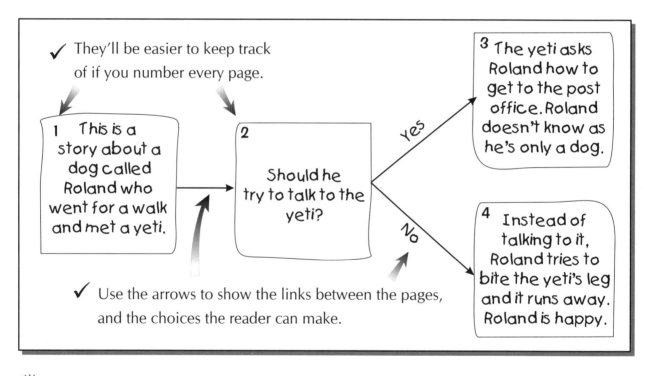

✓ They'll be easier to keep track of if you number every page.

1 This is a story about a dog called Roland who went for a walk and met a yeti.

2 Should he try to talk to the yeti?

yes → 3 The yeti asks Roland how to get to the post office. Roland doesn't know as he's only a dog.

No → 4 Instead of talking to it, Roland tries to bite the yeti's leg and it runs away. Roland is happy.

✓ Use the arrows to show the links between the pages, and the choices the reader can make.

You can make your story as long as you like. My example about the yeti is quite short, but the map can go on for as long as you like — provided it makes sense.

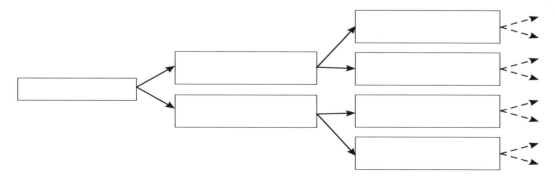

Tell a Story

Now think about the Pictures and Sound:

☼ Think about each page on its own —
decide whether you want to add a picture or a sound to any of them.

☼ Mark on your map where you want any pictures to go.

☼ Mark each bit where you want a sound to be played.

These only have to be rough — it's just to get
you to work out where everything is going to go.

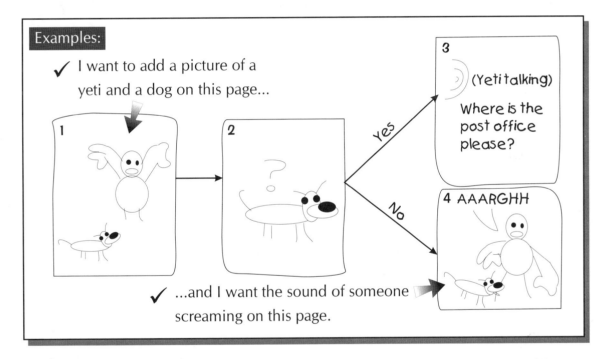

Examples:

✔ I want to add a picture of a
yeti and a dog on this page...

3)) (Yeti talking)

Where is the post office please?

4 AAARGHH

✔ ...and I want the sound of someone
screaming on this page.

☼ Once you've done all this, you're ready to
start making your pages on the computer.

That was the easy bit — putting this on the computer
and making it perfect can take a bit longer.

Remember to think about who's going to read it — don't make your story too complicated.

16

 **Computer Activity**   # Tell a Story

Now you have to turn the pages on your map into an interactive story on your computer.

Make sure you know where you have to start each new 'page'.

- In MS PowerPoint, each page will be on a separate slide.
- In MS Excel, each page could be on a different worksheet.
- In MS Word, each page might be a separate document.

Ask your teacher if you're not sure about this.

Do the easy bits first — add the words and pictures

It's best to make the pages in the order that you numbered them on your map.

 First, type in your text.

   ✓ Make it really easy for people to understand.

   ✓ You can make it look good by making the text different colours and sizes.

 Next, add the pictures.

   ✓ You could use pictures from Clip Art.

   ✓ Or you could use pictures you've drawn yourself.

   ✓ But make sure the pictures don't get in anything's way.

Example: Page 1 of my yeti story might look like this...

This is a story about a dog called Roland who went for a walk and met a yeti.

- Make sure you end up with the same number of pages on the computer as on your map.
- Save all the files you need for your story in the same place so that everything's easy to find — this will include all the files for your pages, all your pictures and all your sounds.

Get your sounds ready:

Here's where the real fun starts.

 You should know what sounds you need — just look back at your map.

   ✓ You could make your own sounds using Windows Sound Recorder (see page 6).

   ✓ Or maybe you can find some cool sounds on a CD-ROM.

Unit 6A — Multimedia Presentation

Tell a Story

Computer Activity

Now it's time to add your buttons:

There are two kinds of button you might need to add to your page:

① Buttons that **play sounds** (by opening a sound file),

② Buttons that let you jump to a **new page** (by opening a new document, or by jumping to a different slide or page in the same document).

4 Whatever kind of button you're adding, you need to type the word, or draw the shape or picture first — then you can make the link.

> You can make a word, a shape or a picture into a button.

The yeti asks Roland how to get to the Post Office. Roland doesn't know as he's only a dog.

Click here to hear the yeti talk

- I've drawn a square for the sound button on page 3 of my story.

- I've also labelled the button so the reader will know what it does.

- Every time there's an arrow on your map, you need to draw a button to link your pages.

- These are the buttons on Page 2 of my story.

- I've used squares for the buttons again.

Should he try to talk to the yeti?

Yes

No

5 Now create the links — see page 8 for more information about this.

✓ Remember: the buttons that play sounds will be linked to other files — the sound files you found or made on page 16.

✓ The buttons that link to other pages may be linked to other files, or to different parts of the same file. It all depends on the software you're using.

If you did all that, you're as clever as ten bears...

You've made an interactive story, but it would have been just as easy to make your own website or multimedia presentation — and how cool is that...

Spreadsheets

You should know a bit about spreadsheets already. But here's a quick reminder if you've forgotten.

Spreadsheets are like tables

Spreadsheets are made of cells arranged in rows and columns.
Cells can contain text, numbers (including money), dates and formulas.

	A	B	C	D	E	F
1	Groceries Shopping List					
2						
3	Item	Cost per item/pack	Number of items	Cost		
4	Chocolate flavoured sprouts	£2.40	1	£2.40		
5	Sundried Cabbage	£3.40	1	£3.40		
6	Mouldy tomatoes	£0.10	10	£1.00		
7	Poodle flavoured dipping chips	£0.97	1	£0.97		
8	Assorted dog flavoured dips	£0.99	3	£2.97		
9	Aubergine mints	£0.30	1	£0.30		
10	Stilton milkshake	£0.69	3	£2.07		
11	Sweaty sock fizzy pop	£1.30	1	£1.30		
12			TOTAL	£14.41		
13						
14						
15						
16						

Spreadsheets are great for doing tables, shopping lists and budgets.

I'm using this one to work out how many groceries I can buy for £15.

You put formulas in to work things out

Formulas are great. Without them, spreadsheets would be pretty pointless really.

Here's four things to know about them:

 1 They let you add, subtract, multiply and divide numbers in different cells.

2 They also let you add up rows or columns of numbers.

 3 All formulas must start with an equals sign **=**.

4 If you change any of the numbers, the formula updates automatically. Wow.

My groceries spreadsheet uses formulas:

Cells D4 to D11 multiply the cost per item by the number of items.

So the formula in **D4** is **=B4*C4** and the formula in **D8** is **=B8*C8**.

Cell D12 contains the formula
= SUM(D4:D11)

This adds up cells D4 to D11 to find the total for that column.

This is the formula bar. When you click on a cell, the formula appears here.

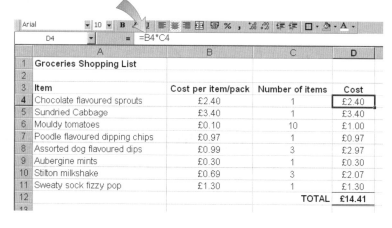

Spreadsheets

① Which of these things could you use a spreadsheet for?

Draw a splodge around each correct answer.

like this

feeding pets

making a shopping list

cleaning the loo

making tables of information

doing calculations

working out a holiday budget

② What type of data do these cells contain?

James is using a spreadsheet to decide how to spend his birthday money.
He has £50 to spend.

	A	B	C	D
1	How I'll spend my birthday money			
2				
3	Item	Cost per item	No of Items	Cost
4	Britney CD singles	£3.99	3	£11.97
5	Britney CD album	£12.99	1	£12.99
6	Britney Posters	£4.99	2	£9.98
7	Magazines with Britney in	£0.75	6	£4.50
8	Britney Stickers	£0.15	5	£0.75
9	Britney's Spaghetti Shapes	£0.79	3	£2.37
10	Britney's Purple Nostril Hair Dye	£1.29	1	£1.29
11	Britney's Zit-zapping Spot Cream	£2.50	1	£2.50
12				
13			Total:	£46.35
14				

For each cell below, say whether it contains **text**, a **number** or a **formula**.

B3 ....   B11 ....   D6 ....

B4 ....   A1 ....   D9 ....

A5 ....   D13 ....   C8 ....

③ What happens when a number is changed?

James finds out that Britney posters are on special offer — now only **£1.99**.
James changes the value in cell **B6** to **1.99**.

Which other cells will change too? ....

James decides to only buy 2 CD singles instead.
Which cell should he change and which ones will change as a result?

He should change cell .... Cells .... will then change.

Maths with Spreadsheets

Another thing that spreadsheets are good for is... well, urr ...maths.

A quick reminder of some easy maths

You probably already know these rectangle formulas, but if you've forgotten...

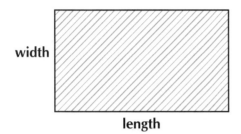

Area is the amount of space a shape takes up.
The **area** of a rectangle is the **length × width**.

Perimeter is the distance round the outside of a shape.
The **perimeter** of a rectangle is **2 × (length + width)**.

You can use spreadsheets like calculators

I've made a spreadsheet to calculate the area and perimeter of any rectangle.

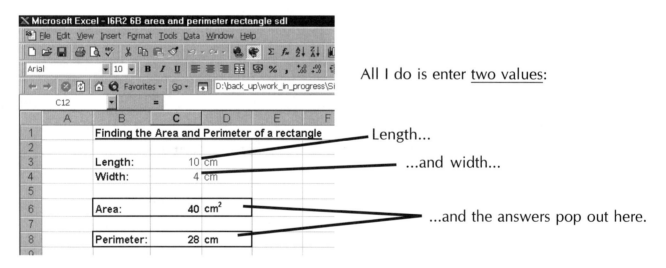

All I do is enter <u>two values</u>:

Length...

...and width...

...and the answers pop out here.

If I change the length or width value, the area and perimeter change automatically. It's magic.

Formulas are the secret

This spreadsheet uses two formulas — one to calculate the area and one to calculate the perimeter.

The area formula is **=C3*C4** and goes in cell **C6**.
It multiplies the length in C3 by the width in C4.

> In spreadsheets, * means **multiply** and / means **divide**.

The perimeter formula is **= 2*(C3 + C4)** and goes in cell **C8**.
It adds the length in C3 to the width in C4 and multiplies this by 2.

Maths with Spreadsheets

① *Unmuddle these sentences about area and perimeter.*

Area space is the amount of up. that a shape takes

....

Perimeter a shape. round the is the distance outside of

....

② *Help me complete these spreadsheets.*

 I'm making a spreadsheet to calculate the area of triangles.

Which cell should I put the formula in? ....

What formula should I put in the cell?

	A	B	C
1	Ace Triangle Calculator		
2			
3	Height:	35	cm
4	Base:	26	cm
5			
6	Area:		cm^2
7			

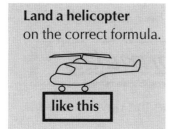

Land a helicopter on the correct formula.

like this

=A3 * A4 / 2   =B3 / B4 * 2   =B3 * B4 / 2

 This spreadsheet will calculate the area of different sized squares.

Which **cell** should I put the formula in? ....

What formula should I type in the cell?

....

	A	B	C	D
1				
2		Funky Square Calculator		
3				
4		Side Length		cm
5				
6				
7		Area:		cm^2
8				

MAKE AN AREA CALCULATOR

Make your own spreadsheet to calculate the area of a rectangle. What happens when you change the length or width value? If you're feeling dead smart, extend your spreadsheet to calculate the area of a triangle and a circle too.

Copying Formulas

Copy and paste is a really handy trick in computing.

It just always seems to work and it can save loads of time.

Sometimes you need loads of formulas

I'm making a multiplication table.

The third column is going to multiply the numbers in the first two columns.

	A	B	C
1			
2	Number A	Number B	Number A × Number B
3	4	1	
4	4	2	
5	4	3	
6	4	4	
7	4	5	
8	4	6	
9	4	7	
10	4	8	
11	4	9	
12	4	10	
13	4	11	
14	4	12	
15			

So I need to put the formula " $= A3 * B3$ " in cell C3.

... and put formulas in all the other cells like this:

$= A4 * B4$

$= A5 * B5$

$= A6 * B6$

$= A7 * B7$

$= A8 * B8$

......

.....

But it's pretty boring because I'm typing almost the same formula every time.

Imagine if my table had 100 rows — it would be a nightmare.

Copy and Paste works great with formulas

But don't have nightmares because copy and paste is going to save the day...

1   **Type** in the first formula (**$= A3 * B3$**).

2   Then **copy and paste** it to the next cell.

Click on the formula and select Copy from the Edit menu.

Then click on the next cell down and select Paste.

SUM			= A3 * B3
	A	B	C
1			
2	Number A	Number B	Number A × Number B	copy
3	4	1	= A3 * B3
4	4	2	
5	4	3		and paste

C14		= A14 * B14
	A	B	C
1			
2	Number A	Number B	Number A × Number B
3	4	1	4
4	4	2	8
5	4	3	12
6	4	4	16
7	4	5	20
8	4	6	24
9	4	7	28
10	4	8	32
11	4	9	36
12	4	10	40
13	4	11	44
14	4	12	48

... and paste

... paste

... paste

... and so on

=A11 * B11 goes here

=A14 * B14 goes here

Now this is the clever bit — the computer changes the formula when I paste it. It puts **$=A4*B4$** into cell **C4**, puts **$=A5*B5$** into **C5** and so on.

3   To complete the table, just keep **pasting** all the way down.

And watch with great wonder and awe as the right formula magically appears each time...

Copying Formulas

① What does copying and pasting save you loads of?

Tick the correct box.

 **time** ☐

 **wine** ☐

 **slime** ☐

② How do you copy and paste cells?

The sentences below are in the wrong order. Write them out in the correct order.

Select **Paste** from the Edit menu. Click where you want it copied to. Click on the cell you want to copy. Select **Copy** from the Edit menu at the top of the screen.

....

....

....

③ How does copying and pasting formulas work?

C3		=	=B3*9	
	A	B	C	D
1				
2		Number A	Number A × 9	
3		1	9	
4		2		
5		3		
6		4		
7		5		
8		6		
9		7		
10		8		
11		9		
12		10		
13		11		
14		12		
15				

This cell contains the formula **= B3 * 9**

If I copy this cell and paste into cell C4, what number will appear there? ....

When I click on cell C4 now, **which of these** formulas will appear in the formula bar?

= B3 * 9   **= B4 * 9**   **= C3 * 9**

A handy tip

You can really speed things up by **pasting** all the cells **in one go**.
Copy the first cell, **select** all the cells you want to paste into and then **paste**.
This means you can do **whole columns** of a table with a single paste.

Creating Charts and Graphs

Reading numbers in a table can be dull and confusing. That's where graphs come in...

You can use spreadsheets to make charts

Here's the spreadsheet from page 18 with my shopping list on.

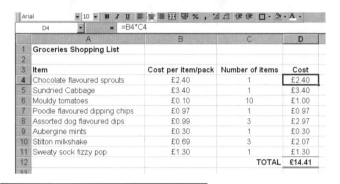

The spreadsheet software can take this table and turn it into a chart. It's clever like that.

I'm going to use it to compare how much money I spend on different foods.

Here's how...

It might be a bit different on your program, but the basic steps will be the same.

 Select the bits you want for your chart.

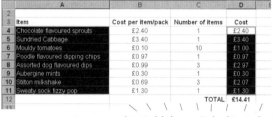

Hold down Ctrl when selecting the second column. This keeps the first column selected.

 Press the chart button .

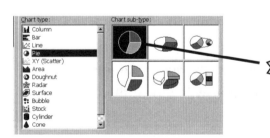

Choose the type of chart.

I'm using a pie chart — they're good for comparing things split into categories. (A bar chart would have worked well too.)

And here's the result — wow...

The computer even puts in a nice key to show what the different sectors are.

(I did choose my own title though.)

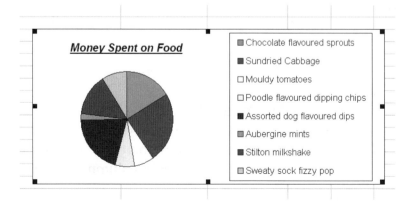

Creating Charts and Graphs

① Which parts of the spreadsheet do I select?

Sarah, Paul and David recorded the time they spent on different evening activities for a week.

	A	B	C	D	E	F
1		Time spent (in hours) on different activities over a week				
2						
3			Sarah	Paul	David	
4		Homework	10	2	6	
5		Eating	6	6	7	
6		Watching TV	3	2	13	
7		Slug chasing	5	2	0	
8		Hedgehog collecting	4	1	2	
9		Emu tickling	2	17	2	
10						

I want a graph showing how Paul spent his time. Which cells should I select for this chart? **Write "hey, cool!"** next to the correct answer.

Cells C3 to E9   **Cells B4 to B9 and cells D4 to D9**

Cells D4 and D9   **Cells C3 to E3 and cells D4 to D9**

② Use the pie charts to answer these questions.

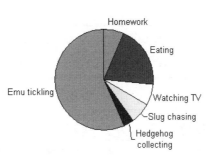

Sarah's activities   **Paul's activities**

I made these two charts from the table above.

Who spent more of their time doing **homework**? ....

Who spent more of their time **chasing slugs**? ....

Which **two** activities did Paul spend **most time** doing?

1. ....   2. ....

Which **three** activities did Sarah spend the **least time** doing?

1. ....   2. ....   3. ....

Creating Charts and Graphs

Line graphs and bar charts are good for weather info

The two tables below contain weather information for the village of Hodgetickle.

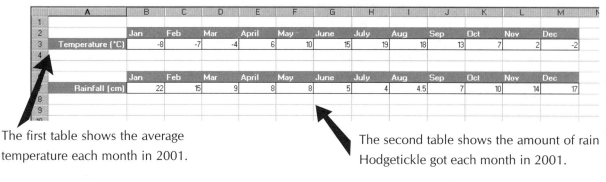

	A	B	C	D	E	F	G	H	I	J	K	L	M
1													
2		Jan	Feb	Mar	April	May	June	July	Aug	Sep	Oct	Nov	Dec
3	Temperature (°C)	-8	-7	-4	6	10	15	19	18	13	7	2	-2
4													
		Jan	Feb	Mar	April	May	June	July	Aug	Sep	Oct	Nov	Dec
	Rainfall (cm)	22	15	9	8	8	5	4	4.5	7	10	14	17
8													
9													

The first table shows the average temperature each month in 2001.

The second table shows the amount of rain Hodgetickle got each month in 2001.

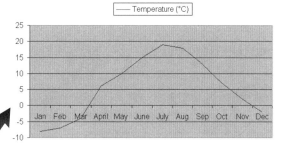

I've put the temperature numbers onto a line graph. Now it's easy to see how the temperature changes over the year.

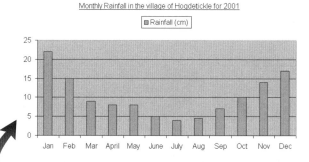

And I've put the rainfall numbers onto a bar chart. It's much clearer than looking at numbers in a table.

It's really easy to make tables into charts and graphs like this. Just select the whole table and press the chart button 📊 .

Scatter graphs are good for tables of numbers

Scatter graphs (and some line graphs) take two columns of numbers and turn them into a set of points on a graph.

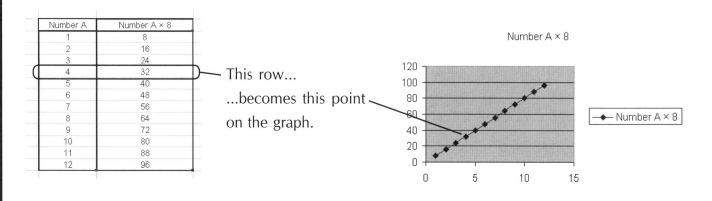

Number A	Number A × 8
1	8
2	16
3	24
4	32
5	40
6	48
7	56
8	64
9	72
10	80
11	88
12	96

This row...

...becomes this point on the graph.

Creating Charts and Graphs

① Which graph works best?

Here are **3 different graphs** showing the **same data**.

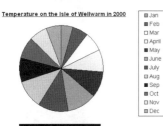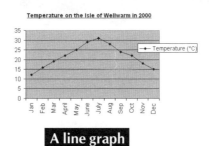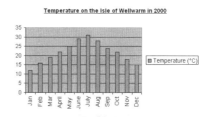

Which graph do you think **works the best**? ....
Explain why you think it's the best.

....

....

Which graph is the **least helpful**? Can you explain why?

....

....

② Which graph should I use for these tables?

Draw a lasso from each table to the best graph to use.

PIE CHART

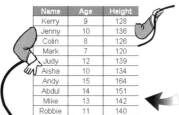

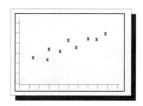

SCATTER GRAPH

I want to be able to use the graph to see if _age_ depends on _height_.

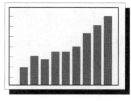

BAR CHART

Unit 6B — Spreadsheet Modelling

Computer Activity

Making Tables and Graphs

In this project you will:

Create tables of numbers and see what kind of graphs they make.

Make some lovely tables of numbers

Here are three incomplete tables.

	A	B
1	X	X × X
2	0	
3	5	
4	10	
5	15	
6	20	
7	25	
8	30	
9	35	
10	40	
11	45	
12	50	
13	55	
14	60	

This column will show "X multiplied by itself" for different values of a number X.

	A	B
1	X	X × 6
2	0	
3	5	
4	10	
5	15	
6	20	
7	25	
8	30	
9	35	
10	40	
11	45	
12	50	
13	55	
14	60	

This column will show "X multiplied by 6" for different values of X.

	A	B
1	X	X + 8
2	0	
3	5	
4	10	
5	15	
6	20	
7	25	
8	30	
9	35	
10	40	
11	45	
12	50	
13	55	
14	60	

This column will show "X + 8" for different values of X.

1. Copy out the **first table**.

   You need to **add formulas** to complete the second column.

2. Click on **cell B2** and type **= A2 * A2** and press Enter.
   This multiplies the number in cell A2 by itself and puts the answer in cell B2.

   > On spreadsheets you need to use * for multiply and / for divide.

3. Now you need to put similar formulas in cells **B3** to **B14**.
   The quick way to do this is to copy the formula in B2 and paste it into cells B3–B14.
   Click on the cell B2, select Copy from the Edit menu, highlight the cells B3 to B14 with the mouse and select Paste from the Edit menu.

4. If you did it right, you should have these numbers in the second column:
   0 25 100 225 400 625 900 1225 1600 2025 2500 3025 3600

Making Tables and Graphs

Make a graph from the table

Now you're going to see what **X × X** looks like on a graph.

The computer can plot points on a graph using the numbers from your table.

The instructions below are for Microsoft Excel but the basic steps are the same in any program.

1. Highlight the two columns of numbers in the table.
   Click on A2 and, holding the mouse button down, drag the cursor down to B14.

	A	B
1	X	X × X
2	0	0
3	5	25
4	10	100
5	15	225
6	20	400
7	25	625
8	30	900
9	35	1225
10	40	1600
11	45	2025
12	50	2500
13	55	3025
14	60	3600
15		
16		

2. Click the new chart button.

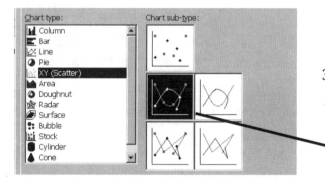

3. Now you need to choose the type of graph. Scatter graphs are best for plotting points, so choose the **XY (Scatter)** option and choose this one. (It joins up all the points with a nice smooth line.)

4. You'll need to choose a title and label for your graph. Your final graph should look something like this:

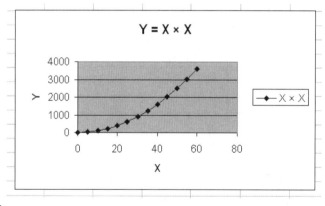

Now make the other tables and graphs

It's time to have a go on your own. Go back and do the same for the other two tables.
You'll need to put one correct formula into each table and then copy it to the other cells.
Then you can make a graph just like above.

When you've finished, answer these questions about the graphs.

Graph	Is it straight or curved?
X × X	....
X × 6	....
X + 8	....

What (roughly) is the value of X × X when X is 53? .... (use the graph)

 **Computer Activity**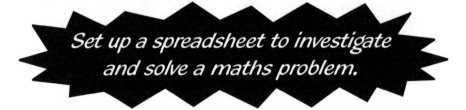

Solve a Tricky Problem

Set up a spreadsheet to investigate and solve a maths problem.

In this project you will:

The Problem

Old uncle Bob has 22 metres of fencing. He is going to use it to build a rectangular pig pen.

He wants the pen to have the biggest area possible for his pigs.

Your task is to find the rectangle that gives the biggest area.

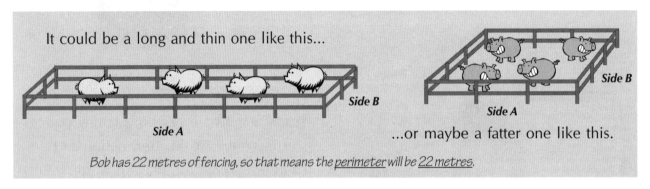

It could be a long and thin one like this...

Side B

Side A

...or maybe a fatter one like this.

Side B

Side A

Bob has 22 metres of fencing, so that means the perimeter will be 22 metres.

Make a table to investigate different possible rectangles

First, you need to make a table like this. (This one isn't complete yet.)

	A	B	C	D	E	F	G	H	I	J	K
1	Side A	1	2	3	4	5	6	7	8	9	10
2	Side B	10	9								
3	Perimeter										
4	Area										

1. **Copy this table** into a new spreadsheet. (Make sure you start from cell A1 like this.)

2. Click on cell B3 and **enter this formula = 2 * (B1 + B2).**
   This adds the lengths of side A and side B and multiplies by 2 to give the perimeter.

3. **Copy and paste** this formula into the other cells in the row (cells C3 to K3).
   If it's worked, the first two perimeter values will be 22.

4. **Complete** the second row by filling in the **missing lengths** for side B.
   Remember — the perimeter must be 22. So each length you put in should give a perimeter of 22. If it doesn't, you've got the length wrong.

5. **Add a formula** to cell B4 to calculate the **area** of the rectangle in column B.

   OK, I'll give you a clue — it's one of these: = B2 * C2   = B1 * B2   = B3 * B5

6. Now **copy and paste** this formula into the other cells in the row (cells C4 to K4).

Solve a Tricky Problem
Computer Activity

Now plot a graph from your results

If everything has gone OK, you will now have a complete table like this.

	A	B	C	D	E	F	G	H	I	J	K
1	Side A	1	2	3	4	5	6	7	8	9	10
2	Side B	10	9	8	7	6	5	4	3	2	1
3	Perimeter	22	22	22	22	22	22	22	22	22	22
4	Area	10	18	24	28	30	30	28	24	18	10

Each column shows a possible rectangle of perimeter 22.
The bottom number is the area of the rectangle.

1. Use your spreadsheet program to **draw a graph**. Use the data in row 1 and row 4 (**Side A** and **Area**) for your graph. You should draw a line graph or a joined-up scatter graph.

If you're using Microsoft Excel
Select the numbers in row 1 with the mouse.
Holding down Ctrl, select the numbers in row 4.
Press the Chart button and choose XY (Scatter).

Area of possible rectangles

(graph with y-axis labelled m², values 0 to 35, x-axis labelled Length of Side A (m), values 0 to 12)

2. Add labels and a title like this.

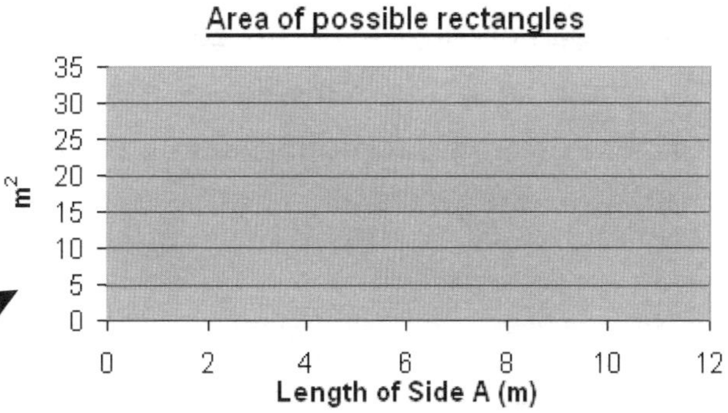

Now use your graph to solve the problem

For the largest area, how long must Side A be? .... metres   *(You can read this answer from the graph.)*

How long is Side B at this point? .... metres   *(Remember, the perimeter must be 22 metres.)*

What special name does this type of rectangle have?   ....

Try again

Dopey Uncle Bob made a mistake.

He actually has 45 m of fencing.

Go back and work out what size and

shape rectangle will give him the

biggest area now.

Draw the rectangle in this box.
Label the sides and put some
smelly pigs in it.

Computer Control

Computers can be used to control different kinds of device. And they can monitor the environment using sensors attached to them. They can also do both those things at the same time.

Computers Can Monitor and Control

① With security lights, computers monitor the surroundings, and turn a light on if they detect movement or body heat.

② Computers can control street lights. When it gets dark in the evening, the lights are turned on automatically. In the morning, they're turned off again.

③ Supermarket fridges and freezers can be controlled by computers. The temperature is monitored, and if it gets too warm, the cooling system is turned on. When it gets cold enough, the system's turned off again.

> In all of these, the environment has to be monitored constantly to see if anything has changed.

Timed Events are Different

Timed events are where the computer turns things on and off at set times. The computer doesn't monitor the environment at all.

Traffic lights often stay red for, say, 1 minute, then go green for 1 minute. This doesn't involve any monitoring — it's a timed event.

But if the traffic lights stay red until a sensor detects a car approaching, then this involves monitoring the road. It is not a timed event.

Make sure you know the difference between...

...timed events and events that happen as a result of a change in the environment.

Computer Control

① This is Lionel — he's a lizard and he monitors flies.

Complete the sentences with words from the 'lizard box' to show how Lionel monitors flies.

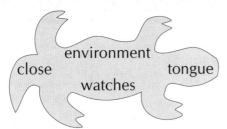

environment
close   tongue
watches

Lionel sits on rocks and .... all the other animals. He watches flies

especially carefully. When a fly comes .... to Lionel, he always does

the same thing — he zaps out his .... and catches the fly. When Lionel

catches a fly like this, he's reacting to his ....

② This is Bert — he's a lizard, but he's a timed lizard.

Bert isn't a monitor lizard — he's a timed lizard. Every 30 seconds he zaps out his tongue and
hopes that a fly is in front of him. Tick the sentences below that you think are true.

☐ Monitor lizards are better at catching flies than timed lizards.

☐ Timed lizards catch more flies.

☐ Bert doesn't eat very much.

③ Think of something that uses monitoring.

Think of a system that uses monitoring to control a process.
Then describe what it monitors and how it reacts to changes in conditions.

System: ....

Monitors: ....

How the system reacts: ....

....

....

Control Hardware and Software

You can do monitoring and controlling from a computer in the classroom.
You just need to attach a few extra bits.

You Need a Control Box, Sensors and Outputs

 The first thing you need is a control box
— this attaches to the back of your computer.

 This has numbered output
sockets to plug things like
lamps and speakers into.

 It also has numbered input
sockets to plug sensors into.

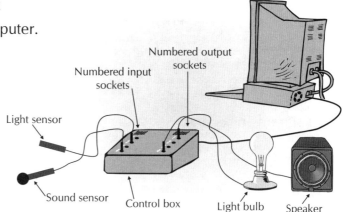

Control Things using a Control Language

Once everything's attached to your computer, you need a way to turn things **on** and **off**.
You do this with a control language.

 Some control languages
need to be typed in.

A simple program
might look like this:

```
Start
Switch on 1
Delay 5
Switch off 1
Stop
```

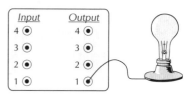

This switches on whatever is plugged into output
socket 1 (a lamp or a speaker etc.).
Then it waits for a while, and switches it off again.

 Other control programs work by getting you to draw a flow chart.

This flow chart does the same thing as the program above.

The main difference is that you have to put each line of your
program in a certain kind of box.

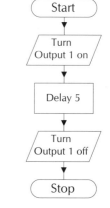

It doesn't matter what control software you have...

They all do the same thing — they just look a bit different, that's all.

Control Hardware and Software

① What will you need?

Circle the item below that will help you connect sensors and outputs to your computer.

a banana skin

bits of egg shell

a small muffin

an old hat

 a control box

② Fill in the gaps with words from the box.

| control language | control box | numbered | flow chart |

To attach outputs to your computer, you need a .... A control box has

.... input and output sockets. You use a ....

to control the output devices and get information from the input devices. Some control

languages have to be typed in, while others let you draw a ....

③ What would I hear from this program?

I have these electronic toys plugged into my control box.
What will I hear when I run the program below? Tick the correct box.

Program:

| Start |
| Switch on 1 |
| Switch on 3 |
| Switch on 4 |
| Switch on 2 |
| Stop |

Fzzzzz — "Can't get you out of my head" — "Go to bed early" — Squawk ☐

"Eat more sprouts" — Quack — Fzzzzz — "I should be so lucky..." ☐

Moooo — "...lucky, lucky, lucky" — "Read more books" — Fzzzzz ☐

"Brush your teeth" — Fzzzzz — "I should be so lucky in love" — Baaah ☐

Control Languages

Control languages use procedures — like in LOGO. Procedures let you break your program into smaller chunks. And there are other things you need to know about control languages too.

Repeat forever... — makes an Endless Loop

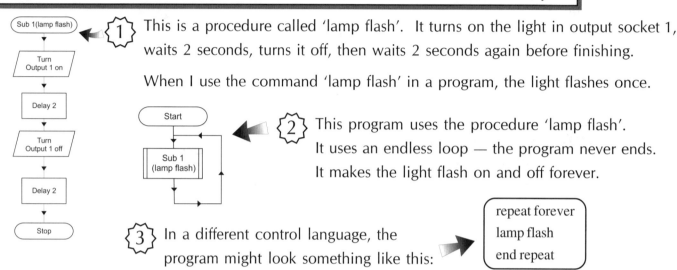

① This is a procedure called 'lamp flash'. It turns on the light in output socket 1, waits 2 seconds, turns it off, then waits 2 seconds again before finishing.

When I use the command 'lamp flash' in a program, the light flashes once.

② This program uses the procedure 'lamp flash'. It uses an endless loop — the program never ends. It makes the light flash on and off forever.

③ In a different control language, the program might look something like this:

```
repeat forever
lamp flash
end repeat
```

A BACKWARDS LOOP in a flow chart is the same as 'REPEAT...' in other control languages.

Check Inputs with a Decision Box or 'If... Then...'

Connecting a switch to your computer means you can make a program that will turn on a light when the switch is pressed.

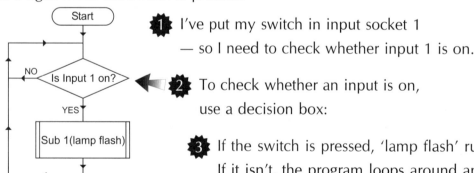

1 I've put my switch in input socket 1 — so I need to check whether input 1 is on.

2 To check whether an input is on, use a decision box:

Decision boxes always have a 'yes path' and a 'no path' leading from them.

3 If the switch is pressed, 'lamp flash' runs and the light flashes. If it isn't, the program loops around and checks the switch again.

```
repeat forever
if input 1 on then lamp flash
end repeat
```

In other control languages, the program might look like this. Instead of a decision box, you use an if... then... statement.

A DECISION BOX in a flow chart is the same as using 'IF... THEN...'.

Now try making this yourself...

Set up a system with a bulb and a switch so that the bulb comes on whenever you press the switch. Test your system by pressing the switch and making sure the bulb comes on every time.

Control Languages

① _These flowers dance when switched on._

Fill in this flow chart to make the flowers dance for 5 seconds and then stop.

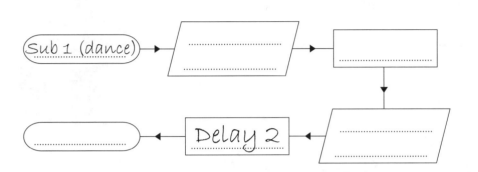

② _Now make them dance forever._

Complete this flow chart to make your flowers keep dancing (with short pauses) forever.

Use your procedure 'dance' from Question 1.

You'll need to add arrows as well.

③ _Dance when I say "Dance, flowers, dance"._

Now I've added a sound sensor. I want the flowers to do a 5-second dance whenever I shout something into the sensor. Complete this flow chart — use your procedure from Question 1.

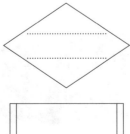

The flowers need to dance when the sound sensor is 'on'.

Unit 6C — Control and Monitoring

Control Devices

Switches aren't the only kind of input device. There are some more interesting ones too.

Light Sensors can Tell when it gets Dark

Light sensors can detect how much light there is.

- You can use a light sensor as a kind of automatic switch — instead of having to press a button to turn a light on, it comes on when it gets dark.

  - This is handy for some things.

Light Sensors are Great for Making a Lighthouse

You can use a light sensor to make a lighthouse.

1. This is how I've set up my control box.

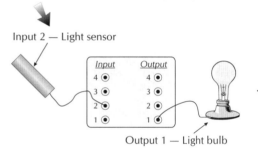

Input 2 — Light sensor

Output 1 — Light bulb

2. I've attached my light sensor to input socket 2, and my light to output socket 1.

3. This procedure 'flash' turns the light in output socket 1 on and off once, with a small delay.

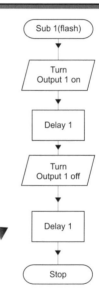

Sub 1(flash)

Turn Output 1 on

Delay 1

Turn Output 1 off

Delay 1

Stop

4. This program will make the light flash when it gets dark, but turn it off when it gets lighter.

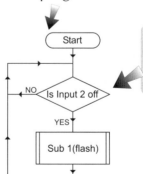

Start

NO — Is Input 2 off

YES

Sub 1(flash)

Because the light sensor is in input socket 2, the decision box in my control program has to check input 2.

I made this lighthouse out of an old toilet roll. It works like a real lighthouse — and looks realistic too.

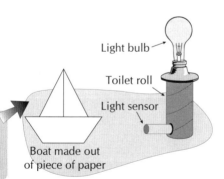

Light bulb

Toilet roll

Light sensor

Boat made out of piece of paper

Now make your own lighthouse...

Use a light sensor and a bulb (and an old toilet roll, if you like) to make a lighthouse like this one. The bulb needs to flash when it gets dark. Test your lighthouse carefully.

By the way — I think 'lighthouse' is a stupid name....

...because I reckon they must be really heavy.

Control Devices

1 You can use sensors as switches.

Sensors can be used to turn things on automatically in certain conditions.
Match each situation below to the kind of sensor you'd need.

To turn something on...

...you'd need...

1. When it gets dark...

a sound sensor

2. When it gets noisy...

3. When it gets cold...

a temperature sensor

4. When it gets light...

5. When it gets too quiet...

a light sensor

2 I have an Alien Death Ray.

To prevent burglaries, I've attached my Alien Death Ray to a light sensor. As soon as a burglar switches on the lights, they get a small electric shock. Fill in the flow chart below to show how the anti-burglar system works.

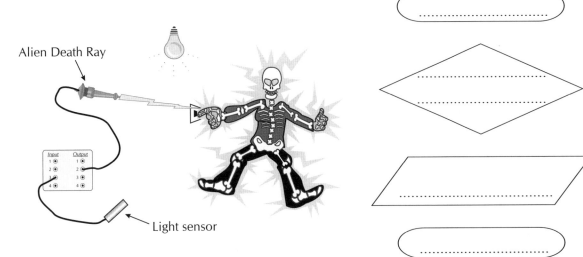

Alien Death Ray

Light sensor

3 What shall I call my robot dog?

He's very friendly, but sometimes gets confused and eats people.
Think of a good name for him.

....

 **Computer Activity**

A Super Lighthouse

You'll need a control box, 2 light sensors and a bulb for this project.

In this project you will:

Build a super-advanced lighthouse.

Lighthouses are great — when it gets dark they shine a big light so that ships know where dangerous rocks are. But when it's foggy as well, you need a super-advanced lighthouse.

A super-advanced lighthouse has a foghorn as well

A super-advanced lighthouse can keep ships safe at night when it's foggy as well.
They do this by detecting the fog, and sounding a really loud foghorn that far-off ships can hear.

During the day, the light and foghorn are off.

At night, the light flashes but the foghorn stays off.

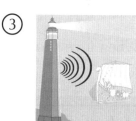

On foggy nights, the light flashes and the foghorn sounds on and off.

This is how you make a night-time fog detector...

You need 2 light sensors separated by a screen that doesn't let light through (you could use a piece of card), and a weak light bulb that's permanently switched on.

 Light sensor 1

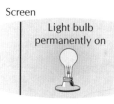 Screen / Light bulb permanently on

 Light sensor 2

1. Light sensor 1 detects whether it's night or day by sensing how much light there is.
2. At night, light sensor 1 doesn't detect much light, so it's 'off'.
   (The screen stops it sensing light from the bulb.)
3. The light bulb in front of sensor 2 is always on, and means that sensor 2 does detect light — even at night.
4. But when it gets foggy, the fog stops the light from the weak bulb reaching light sensor 2, so that sensor goes 'off' too.

Here's how you can simulate night and fog in the classroom using these sensors.
You don't even need the screen if you're using your thumb to cover the sensors.

① Daytime, not foggy.   ② Night, not foggy.   ③ Night, foggy.

A Super Lighthouse

Write your output procedures

You'll need 3 procedures for this project:

- one for when it's daytime — both the light and the foghorn should be switched off.
- one for when it's night, but not foggy — the light should flash on and off, but the foghorn should be off.
- one for when it's night and foggy — the light and foghorn should both go on and off.

Here's my procedure that flashes the light and sounds the horn on a foggy night.

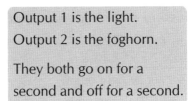

Output 1 is the light.
Output 2 is the foghorn.

They both go on for a second and off for a second.

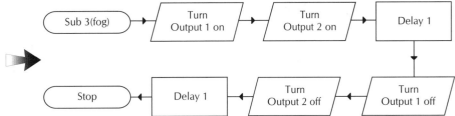

Write the main program

It can be useful to do a flow chart in English, rather than your control language — it makes it easier to think about what you're doing. Then it's easy to turn this into control language.

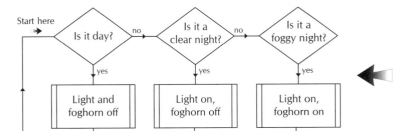

This should work as my main program. Now all I have to do is turn this into control language.

Test your program

Once you've written the program, you have to test it to make sure it does what you want. The easiest way is with a table.

TEST IN PROGRESS

Conditions	What should happen	What actually happens
Day	Light and foghorn off	
Night, no fog	Light flashing, foghorn off	
Night, with fog	Light flashing, foghorn going on and off	

 Write what should happen in different situations, and then what actually happens when you run your program — they should be the same.

 If there's a problem, you'll need to change your program. Your table should help you work out where the problem is.

More Input Devices

You can attach more than one input device to a computer — sounds fun.

Pressure Pads are a Different Kind of Switch

When someone walks on the first pressure pad, the door opens...

...and when they walk on the second one, the door closes.

- This automatic entrance door uses pressure pads to control when it opens and closes.

  - When somebody treads on the pressure pad outside, a signal is sent to a motor, which opens the door.

    - When they tread on the pressure pad inside, another signal is sent to the motor to close the door.

Instead of a pressure pad, a heat sensor or light beam could be used to detect when somebody is approaching.

Use Procedures to Control an Automatic Door

These two procedures are called 'open' and 'close' — they control the door.

The procedure called 'open' turns Motor A forward to open the door — the motor runs for half a second and is then switched off.

The procedure 'close' reverses Motor A to close the door.

Then Use these Procedures in a Program

This is the program that actually controls the door. Make sure you can follow it all.

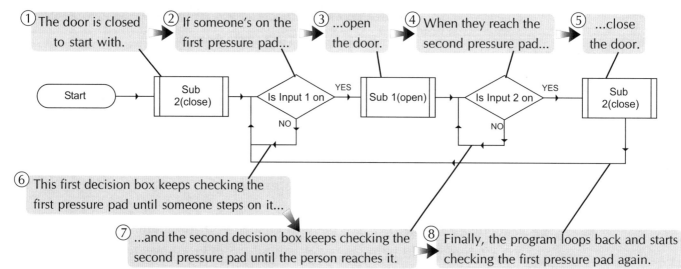

① The door is closed to start with.
② If someone's on the first pressure pad...
③ ...open the door.
④ When they reach the second pressure pad...
⑤ ...close the door.
⑥ This first decision box keeps checking the first pressure pad until someone steps on it...
⑦ ...and the second decision box keeps checking the second pressure pad until the person reaches it.
⑧ Finally, the program loops back and starts checking the first pressure pad again.

More Input Devices

① This is how a supermarket checkout works.

The light beam on the conveyor belt is always on. When the light sensor detects the light, the motor is switched on and the conveyor belt moves. When an item of shopping moves in front of the light, the motor is stopped. Complete the flow chart for this system.

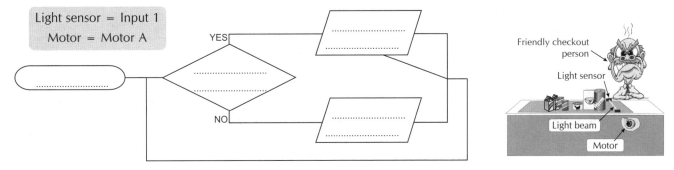

Light sensor = Input 1
Motor = Motor A

YES

NO

Friendly checkout person
Light sensor
Light beam
Motor

② Eric the mouse has designed this simple cat trap.

1. When Eric the mouse is being chased by a cat, he runs across the light beam.
2. The light sensor (Input 1) detects that the light beam has been broken.
3. This causes Motor A to be turned forward, which turns the cable reel and lifts the cat-proof net.
4. When Stanley the cat crosses the light beam, the power to the electromagnet (Output 3) is switched off, which causes the carving knife to fall and cut the cable.
5. This makes the net fall, which catches the cat.

Complete the flow chart for this system.

Is input 1 on   YES

NO

YES

NO

Cat-proof net
Cable reel
Motor A
Metal plate
Stanley
Carving knife
Light sensor
— **Input 1**
Electromagnet
(usually switched on)
— **Output 3**
Eric
Light beam
(always on)

Make an automatic deer... *(Or an automatic door, if you'd prefer)*

Make an automatic door using two inputs. The first input should open the door, and the second input should close it. You could use sound sensors as your inputs (so that the door opens and closes when you shout at it), or some other type of sensor. Test your door carefully.

44

Computer Activity — *Build a Security System*

You'll need a control box, together with various output and input devices.

In this project you will:

Design a home security system.

What you need to do

> ✓ Think of some ways you could improve security in someone's house.
> ✓ Decide: (i) what sensors you need,
>   (ii) what will happen if the sensors are triggered — e.g. an alarm might ring.
> ✓ Your system will also turn a light on automatically when it gets dark, and turn it back off when it gets lighter — to make burglars think someone's still awake.

Decide what sensors you're going to need...

The first thing you need to do is decide what your security system is going to do. This will help you decide what kinds of sensor you need.

- An outside light sensor will detect when it gets dark.

  - You could have a switch on the window that's triggered when the window opens.

    - A pressure pad by the door will detect anyone entering the house.

      - A heat sensor might be able to detect an intruder's body heat.

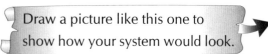

Draw a picture like this one to show how your system would look.

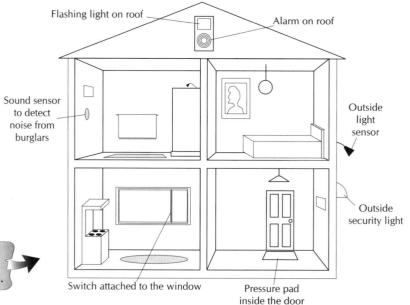

Flashing light on roof — Alarm on roof — Sound sensor to detect noise from burglars — Outside light sensor — Outside security light — Switch attached to the window — Pressure pad inside the door

...and what will happen afterwards

You need to decide what will happen when any of the sensors are triggered.

- When the outside light sensor detects that it's dark, you need to turn on an inside light.

  - If someone's found inside the house, you need to sound the alarm:
    (i) Perhaps a light on the roof will start to flash.
    (ii) Maybe an alarm will go off.
    (iii) You could turn all of the inside lights on.

Build a Security System
Computer Activity

Now list your inputs and outputs

Make a table of all the inputs and outputs that you'll have in your control box.

Inputs	
Input 1	Outside light sensor
Input 2	Sound sensor
Input 3	Pressure pad by front door
Input 4	Switch on kitchen window

Outputs	
Output 1	Downstairs light
Output 2	Upstairs light
Output 3	Alarm on roof
Output 4	Flashing light on roof

It's best to make a table showing what your security system should do

Make a table like this one — give your table 3 columns.

✸ In the first column, write down the things that might happen
— e.g. the pressure pad might detect someone entering the house.

✸ In the second column, write down what your system should do if this happens.

✸ Leave the third column blank — when you've written your control program and need to test it, this is where you can write down what your system actually does.

If this happens...	...the system <u>should</u> do this.	The system <u>actually</u> does this.
Light outside, no sensors set off	All outputs off	
Gets dark outside	Downstairs light comes on	
Gets light outside	Downstairs light is turned off	
Sound sensor triggered	All inside lights on, alarm should go on and roof light should flash on and off	
Pressure pad triggered		
Kitchen window sensor triggered		

Build a model

Connect all your sensors to your control box — use your input and output tables to make sure you put all the sensors and output devices into the right sockets.

☹ It doesn't matter if you don't have a pressure pad or some other type of sensor — you can just use a <u>switch</u> instead.

☺ If you want, you can make a model of your house. Fix all the input and output devices to your model. Try to make it as realistic as my model.

(Only joking.)

Heh heh heh. That was all easy — now it gets much harder.

Write the output procedures

Things are easier if you write a separate procedure for each output. I need a procedure to control the downstairs light, and a separate procedure for when an intruder is detected.

1. The downstairs light comes on when the outside light sensor detects that it's getting dark.

   This light then needs to be switched off when it gets light, so I'll make a procedure for that too.

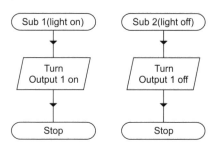

2. If something is detected by one of the other 3 sensors, it means that someone's in the house. If this happens I want all the output devices to be activated.

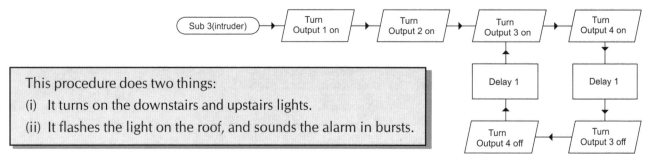

This procedure does two things:
(i) It turns on the downstairs and upstairs lights.
(ii) It flashes the light on the roof, and sounds the alarm in bursts.

Write the main checking program

Writing the main checking program can be a bit tricky. It's best not to rush it.
This is how mine looks.

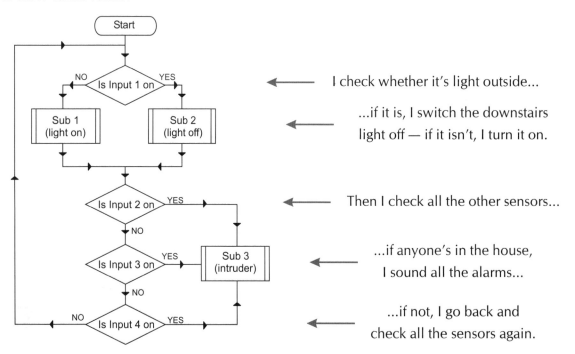

I check whether it's light outside...

...if it is, I switch the downstairs light off — if it isn't, I turn it on.

Then I check all the other sensors...

...if anyone's in the house, I sound all the alarms...

...if not, I go back and check all the sensors again.

Build a Security System

Computer Activity

Testing the system — does it do what it's supposed to?

You've written the program to control your burglar alarm system, but you need to find out if it works like it's supposed to. So you need to test it.

✸ Use your table from page 45. Run your program and see what your system does in each situation from column 1.

✸ If it doesn't do what it's supposed to, you'll need to change your program. It can be pretty hard to work out what to change sometimes. Try asking yourself these questions:

> 1. Does anything at all happen when I trigger the sensor?
>   - If the answer's 'no', then your main checking program might have a problem — perhaps there's something wrong with a decision box.
>   - Or perhaps your program has a loop (see page 36) that means the sensor's never checked.
>   - Or maybe that output procedure has a mistake in it.
> 2. Does the wrong thing happen when you trigger a sensor?
>   - If the answer's 'yes', there's probably a problem with an output procedure.

This bit can be a nightmare — don't worry if you need to try a few different things before you get it to work properly.

Possible improvements you could make

This is a tough project, but when you get your system working you still haven't quite finished. Try to think of any useful improvements you'd like to make to your system.

? Maybe you could add a 'master switch' so that the whole system is only activated when the switch is on. This would also let you turn all the alarms off when the police arrive and arrest the intruder.

? Maybe you could add an outside sensor (maybe a movement sensor or pressure pad) to detect when someone comes near the house, and use it to turn on an outside security light — and then turn it off when they go further away.

? Or perhaps you could use the outside light sensor to turn the whole system on only when it gets dark and everyone's in bed.

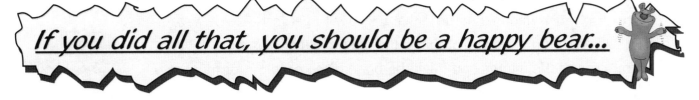

If you did all that, you should be a happy bear...

Finding Information

Doing research used to mean sitting in a library with loads of books and getting bored. Now there are different ways of learning things that can be kinda cool...

There are Loads of Ways to Find Information

You can read <u>newspapers</u> and <u>encyclopedias</u>.

You can buy <u>magazines</u> about particular subjects — e.g. "Dancing Badgers", "Accountants' Monthly" or "Baboon and Elephant Biweekly".

You can use <u>CD-ROMs</u> that show different things using multimedia. Basically, it's more fun because of all the sounds, pictures and videos...

B and E

This issue:
How to find heels that don't rub a monkey.

Bringing the beauty out of your beast...

There's Lots on the Internet too

Most newspapers have their own websites. In fact, lots of businesses and other organisations have websites (e.g. banks, museums, tourist offices etc...).

CGP —
Coconut Gibbon Patrol
Working to keep your coconuts monkey-free

Website addresses usually look a bit like this:
http://www.crazyinthecoconut.co.uk
(The proper name is a **URL** — there'll be more about URLs later...)

Sometimes newspaper articles will show a website address at the end of the text, so you know where to go on the Internet to find out more about the subject.

<u>A REALLY COOL THING ABOUT USING THE INTERNET FOR RESEARCH IS:</u>

There's a huge amount of information on the Internet — there's bound to be something there that will be useful.

You're a nut...

<u>A REALLY BAD THING ABOUT USING THE INTERNET FOR RESEARCH IS:</u>

There's <u>so</u> much information on it that it's easy to get lost — you can waste time looking at things that aren't actually useful. Also, some of the information might be <u>biased</u> (see page 52 for more info.)

That boy needs therapy...

Finding Information

① List 4 places where you can find information.

1. ....

2. ....

3. ....

4. ....

② Fill in the blanks with the right words.

monkeys   website   avalanches

organisations

website addresses

Most .... have their own

.... You can often see their

.... in adverts —

the proper name for these is a ....

URL

coconut

Primate seeking coconut-carrying ape.
Have own car. Will travel. Anything to
save me from these blasted fancy
dress parties...

③ Name a good and a bad thing about using the Internet for research.

Good Thing: ....

....

Bad Thing: ....

....

Understanding Information

Here's a few things to think about when you're trying to find useful information...

Make Sure You Know What You're Looking At

- Have a look at this picture of a dog and read the piece of text next to it.

This dog dragged a 10-year-old boy called Alec to safety from a burning house.

- Seems like a pretty cool dog to me. Now look at the one below and read the text.

This dog bit 178 old ladies' legs last month, as well as biting my arm and eating my pet rabbit.

- If you hadn't read either bit of text, you might think that both dogs were the same.

Having a quick look at the picture isn't enough. It's vital to understand all the information in front of you...

...then you won't get bitten.

Traffic Wardens are made of Jam

The same thing goes for titles. This bit isn't about traffic wardens or jam, although the title says so. This picture isn't anything to do with the rest of the page either...

Think about What it's Saying

Now look at this piece of text:

Marilyn Monroe thought that plum jam was better than all the other types of jam like strawberry or raspberry or chuckberry. Plum jam was her favourite type of jam because it was made of plums and not gooseberries or strawberries.

All it says is that Marilyn Monroe's favourite jam was plum — the rest is just repeating itself.

- This applies to any kind of information you can think of (e.g. newspaper stories, photos, graphs, Internet pages etc...). You have to really think about what it's telling you.

- So, don't just print or copy something because it *seems* helpful — read it all to see if it's worth it.

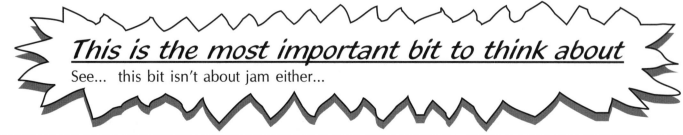

This is the most important bit to think about

See... this bit isn't about jam either...

Understanding Information

① Which of the following sentences contradict themselves?

Put a big cross by the sentences that are <u>silly</u>, and a big tick next to the ones that aren't.

> I don't know what you're complaining about. At least your trousers reach your ankles.

☐ My grandpa is a tall, white-haired, shortish old bald man.

☐ Christopher Columbus sailed to America in 1492.

☐ Girls called Jess are taller than girls called Poppy.

☐ The first day of autumn is also the last day of winter.

☐ Soup should be seen and not heard.

② Pick out the three key points made in this paragraph.

I really enjoy sailing because it makes me happy and makes me enjoy myself. I've sailed since I was 7 and this means that I've been doing it for ages now. This is because I really enjoy it. I enjoy it so much it makes me never want to stop enjoying it. I sail in my friend's boat and I always enjoy myself loads.

1. ....

2. ....

3. ....

③ What's your favourite jam?

....

Different Points of View

Not All Information is Reliable

Information comes from all sorts of different places, but you can't always be sure that it's reliable. This is especially true for websites because:

- Anyone can set up their own website.
- There aren't any rules for what you can and can't say on your own site.
- This means you can say whatever you want.

This sounds pretty cool really, but there's a massive problem — it means you can't trust everything you read.

Look out for Biased Information

If information is **biased**, it means that it's really <u>for</u> or <u>against</u> something (e.g. a Man United fan's website might be really positive about Manchester United but really against Liverpool).

It can sometimes be quite tricky to work out if something is biased or not. Everyone has their own opinion, and will try to make you think theirs is the right one.

Read these two different descriptions of the same event:

HOW I SURVIVED A CAT ATTACK

I was attacked by a cat for no reason. It bent my cage and stole my water bottle. I was really frightened by it all. I'm the victim here.

I WAS HIT BY AN EVIL HAMSTER

The evil hamster made me attack it. It threw its water bottle at my head and it hurt me so much I almost fainted. I don't remember much. I'm the victim here.

They can't both be true because they contradict each other. It's possible that the cat attacked the hamster and damaged the cage after having a water bottle thrown at its head.

The point is that **you don't know for sure**. You have to do your best with what you're given.

If in doubt, Compare it with a Different Source

Ask yourself these questions to check for bias —

— Who wrote it?
— What is it saying?
— Could there be another side to the story?
— What can I compare it with?

THE CGP FILES The Truth is Out There...

BEWARE OF BELIEVING EVERYTHING YOU READ

Different Points of View

① Why can't you trust everything you read on a website?

Draw a star around the ones you think are good answers

Like this:

a — Anyone can write their own webpages.

b — There aren't any rules about what gets written onto websites.

c — Websites are on a computer.

d — The Internet is made of cheese.

② What does "biased information" mean?

Does it mean that the information is

Why did the Moon eat a Mars? It couldn't find the Milky Way.

What a terrible joke...

— definitely true   ☐

— definitely not true   ☐

— for or against something   ☐

— made of cheese   ☐

③ Read this bit of text and answer the questions below.

> I was brought up to believe that peanut butter and jam sandwiches are the most amazing sandwiches on Earth. I've never tried any other type of sandwich, but I know that I hate all other sandwiches, especially cucumber ones. People who don't eat peanut butter are weird.

1) Is this piece of text biased? ....

2) Why do you think this is? (Tick the right one.)

☐ It is clearly in favour of peanut butter and jam sandwiches.

☐ It is made up of facts which are true.

Getting the Right Information

You can Find Internet pages with a Favourites List

Using a **favourites list** is a way to save website addresses to your computer — it's a really easy way to get to websites on the Internet. Your school's probably got its own list of favourite sites.

Here's how to find the favourites list:

Click on "Favourites" on the toolbar
(or else go to the "Favourites" menu at the top).

Clicking on either will bring up a list of sites.
(I'm sure yours are more fun than mine...)

Just click on one of them, and you'll
be taken straight to the page.

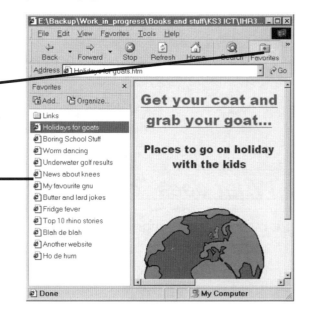

It's useful to Print the Pages you Need

Not *that* sort of prints...

Printing pages from the Internet is a doddle too...

You can either — a) go to "Print" on the File menu (like in a Word document)

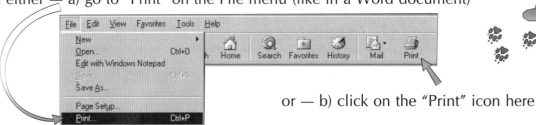

or — b) click on the "Print" icon here

Highlighting is Good

The best bit about printing pages is you can mark out the key bits of information for yourself with a pen.

> Blah blah blah blah blah blah blah blah kind of like being able to highlight this bit blah blah blah blah blah blah blah blah blah...

This is good because — it's easier to see what key points are being made.
— it's quicker to go over them again.

Getting the Right Information

① Give 2 ways of opening the Favourites menu.

1. ....

2. ....

② Give two reasons why highlighting is a good thing to do.

1. ....

2. ....

③ Practise highlighting the important bits of this newspaper article about an iguana.

Britain's first ever case of assault with an iguana went to court yesterday. The reptile, known as Igwig, is an iguana who sat watching the trial quietly from inside his tank. His owner looked confused as she was questioned about the iguana sitting in a tank next to her. Policemen said that Igwig had been mistaken for a scarf wrapped around his owner's neck, until she removed him and threw him at them. The policemen who had been there were asked more questions. The iguana continued to sit silently in his tank. The owner was allowed to leave with Igwig at the end of the day.

Now go and find an interesting site to print...

Look at the list of websites on your school computer's favourites list. Visit some of the sites and look for an interesting fact on one of the pages. When you find an interesting fact, print that web page out, and then use a highlighter pen to highlight your fact. Then make a list of the most interesting facts in the world.

Search Engines

If you want to find a website that isn't already on your favourites list, you can use a **search engine** to find what you want.

Searching the Internet is like Searching a CD-ROM

Search engines work the same way as searches on a CD-ROM. There are lots of different search engines you can use (e.g. Yahoo, MSN, Altavista etc...), but they all look something like this:

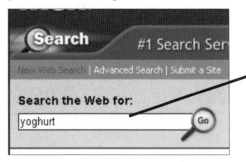

There's a box where you can type in what you want to look for and click on "Go".

(You might have to click on "Search" on some search engines.)

Each Result is called a "Hit"

The search should only take a couple of seconds.

Then the search engine will show you all the sites it found.

Each result is called a **hit**.

It will show the hits in a list like this one.

Searches using One Word are about as useful as putting a Duck in an Elephant Suit...

The main problem with these results is that there's so many of them. In the example above, there were 40 386 hits.

It would take ages to go through them all (and most of them would be useless anyway) — the whole point about the Internet is that it's meant to be quick and easy to use.

The golden rule is not to search for one word only (especially not "yoghurt" — that's just silly). You need to think about how to make your searches **more precise**.

This isn't exactly what I had in mind...

Search Engines

① What is a Search Engine?

Tick the right answer

☐ A way of searching for information on the Internet

☐ A way of searching for books in a library

☐ A way of stuffing a duck into an elephant suit

② What is a Hit?

Tick the right answer

☐ A result from a search using a search engine

☐ The result of pressing the keys on your keyboard really hard

☐ The noise the duck made on entry

③ What's wrong with doing a search using only one word?

....

....

Try searching at different times during the week...

Choose a subject you're interested in that you can search for using one word, e.g. "Oasis", "football" or "cheese".

Then use 3 different search engines and look for your word at different times during the week: e.g. **(i)** when you first start lessons on Monday morning, **(ii)** just after lunch on Wednesday, and **(iii)** just before school finishes on Friday. Write how many 'hits' you get from the different search engines at these different times. Which search engine has the most 'hits'? Do any of the search engines give you a different number of hits at different times? Which one varies most?

Useful Ways to Search

Searching with just one word can be pretty useless. The computer can only work with the information you give it.

Use the Word "and" in your Searches

The trick to getting better search results is to tell the computer more about what you're looking for.

If you use the word "and" in your searches, it'll narrow down the results.

e.g. If you wanted to know about smelly cheeses, you could type this into the search box:
smelly and cheese . The search engine would only look for pages with **both** words in.

This makes your searches twice as good as just typing one word in.

You can type in as many words as you like, as long as you put **"and"** in between them.

e.g. smelly and cheese and french and old
would narrow the results down even more...

This smells worse than your minging feet...

Choose your Words Carefully

Some words get better results than others. That's because they're more **specific**.

If you want to find out about a particular **type** of thing,
then make sure you type its **name** in (e.g. if I want to know about
the size of a velociraptor's teeth, I'll get better results by searching
for "velociraptor and teeth" than by typing "dinosaur").

I like Gorgonzola

Skimming through Results

You need to practise **skimming** through results.

* This means trying to look through lists of titles quickly and judging if they look useful or not — you can do this by picking out the key words.

e.g. No. 33 is a puzzle, so it won't have any information.
No. 34 is about dentistry. I can ignore both of those.

* This is a good trick to learn because you can skip the useless ones and waste less time.

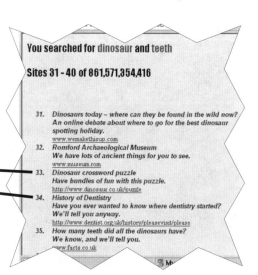

You searched for dinosaur and teeth

Sites 31 - 40 of 861,571,354,416

31. Dinosaurs today – where can they be found in the wild now?
An online debate about where to go for the best dinosaur spotting holiday.
www.wemakethisup.com
32. Romford Archaeological Museum
We have lots of ancient things for you to see.
www.museum.rom
33. Dinosaur crossword puzzle
Have bundles of fun with this puzzle.
http://www.dinosaur.co.uk/puzzle
34. History of Dentistry
Have you ever wanted to know where dentistry started?
We'll tell you anyway.
http://www.dentist.org.uk/history/pleasevisit/please
35. How many teeth did all the dinosaurs have?
We know, and we'll tell you.
www.facts.co.uk

Useful Ways to Search

① Which of these words will help narrow down your results?

(Draw a circle round the right one)

IF   BUT   BUTTER

JAM   AND   GERONIMO

② Which of these searches would be the best one for finding out how to make chicken stew?

- [ ] Chicken
- [ ] Chicken and Stew and Recipe
- [ ] Traffic Wardens are made of jam
- [ ] Stuart and the Chicken

(Actually, you're all wrong — you make a chicken stew by stomping on its foot then running away)

Try your own "AND" search...

Choose two words connected with a topic you're studying at school — your teacher will be able to give you some suggestions for this.
For example, I could use "robin" and "hood".

Now use a search engine to search for each of your words on their own.
So I'd do a search for "robin", and then I'd do a search for "hood".
Write down the number of hits you get for each word.

Now do an AND search for your two words, e.g. "robin AND hood".
How many hits do you get this time? Are the websites similar to before?

Trailing Ideas

You can also search the Internet by clicking on buttons...

You can use hyperlink buttons to surf the net

Most websites have buttons on them that link to other webpages when you click on them.

- These are called **hyperlink buttons** (like on multimedia encyclopedia CD-ROMs) and you can use them to jump from website to website.

  Music brings me out of my shell

    - You can use them to **trail an idea** — you follow interesting links to useful pages you never even knew were there.

        - Another name for this is **surfing the Internet**, which is weird because it's not wet and you don't use a board. But anyway...

My tortoise has started singing Westlife songs. I want to find a website that can tell me what's wrong with her. All I have is the website address for the place I bought her bedding from.

By following these links, I can trail an idea until I find a link to a page that is useful.

There are good and bad things about trailing ideas

Good Things:

1. It can be quicker than skimming through results from a search engine.

2. It's easy to see where links will take you.

3. You can find interesting information that you wouldn't have known to look for.

Bad Things:

1. It's really easy to get lost.

2. You need to have a good place to start.

3. You can sometimes spend ages trailing an idea without finding anything you can use.

Let's see you back out of this one...

Remember that clicking the "BACK" button will take you back to the previous page.

Trailing Ideas

1 Fill in the blanks with the right words.

surfing

buttons

trail

skiing

Most websites have ....

on them that link to other pages. You can use them to

destroy

.... Another name for this

is .... the Internet.

hide

hyperlink

an

idea

2 List 3 good things about trailing ideas.

1. ....

2. ....

3. ....

3 List 3 bad things about trailing ideas.

1. ....

2. ....

3. ....

Bookmarking Sites

I mentioned URLs at the start of the section — ages ago... Well, here they are again:

A URL is the Address of a Website

I expect you've seen loads of URLs. They look like this:

>http://www.guardian.co.uk

A URL is the <u>address</u> of a website. If you type it into the "Address" box at the top of the page and hit "Enter", you'll be taken straight to it.

This is useful if you've seen the URL written down somewhere (like on the telly or a poster) and want to **get to it quickly** without messing around with search engines.

You can Bookmark your Favourite Sites

Typing the whole URL in each time can be tricky — if you get any of it wrong, it won't work.

But, you can **bookmark** the websites that you use the most, so you can get to them more quickly.

This adds them to the **favourites list** — see page 54 for more about this.

Here's how you bookmark a website:

1. Go to the page you want to bookmark.

2. Click on "Favourites" on the toolbar (or the "Favourites" menu at the very top).

3. Click on "Add" (or "Add to Favourites").

4. This box will appear with the name of the webpage already typed in for you.

5. Choose which folder you want to save it in and click OK.

Creating a New Folder for your Bookmarks

You can keep your bookmarks organised by putting them in specific folders (e.g. one for jam sites, one for jokes sites etc...). This is how you make a new folder:

1. Click on the "New Folder" button in the "Add Favourite" box.

2. Type in the name of your new folder and click OK.

3. Make sure your new folder is selected and click OK.

Bookmarking Sites

① What is a URL?

....

② Where on a webpage can you type in a URL?

....

③ Fill in the blanks using these words.

"Add"

"Favourites"

pig

"Okay"

pig

folder

pig

page

bookmark

pig

How to ..... *bookmark* ..... a website:

Once you're on the right .... ,

just click on .... and then

.... Select which

.... you'd like to

save it in, then click on ....

Please don't bring me into this — I've got me own problems...

...There's a bear back there with a gun...

Trail an idea and bookmark the best site you find...

Your teacher will pick a website for your class to start at — everybody in the class has to use the same website. Then follow the most interesting hyperlinks you see until you find a really cool website — bookmark this site in a folder called "Fab and Groovy". When everybody has bookmarked a site, try to guess who chose which site.

Copying and Pasting Stuff

You can Copy things from an Internet Page and Paste them into Your Own Document

You can **print** stuff off the Internet, but you can also **copy** bits (e.g. photos or bits of text) and **paste** them into a document (e.g. like Word, or Excel...).

But see page 66 about <u>copyright</u> before you do this.

This is useful if you want to use things in a computer presentation of your own. It's a lot easier than cutting and gluing bits of printed pages together.

Here's how you do it:

— First, open up the document you want your copied bit to end up in.

— Then get on the Internet and **<u>RIGHT-CLICK</u>** on the thing you want to copy (like our logo, for example).

— This menu will appear, so select "Copy".

> Guess not everything is worth copying ...

— Now go back into your document and then **<u>RIGHT-CLICK</u>** anywhere on the page.

— Then just click on "Paste" and the copy will appear as if by magic. Or possibly science.

<u>THE SAME GOES FOR TEXT — JUST REMEMBER TO HIGHLIGHT THE RIGHT BITS FIRST</u>

You Won't Always Be Able To Copy Things

This doesn't always work. Sometimes all that will get copied is the URL, rather than the picture or piece of text you actually wanted. Your page will just look like this:

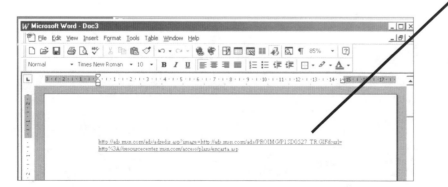

There are lots of different reasons why this might happen — the main thing is that you'll need to copy something different...

Sorry.

Copying and Pasting Stuff

① Give 2 reasons why it's good to "copy and paste" stuff.

1. ....

2. ....

② Put these steps for "copy and pasting" into the right order.

I've done the first one for you...

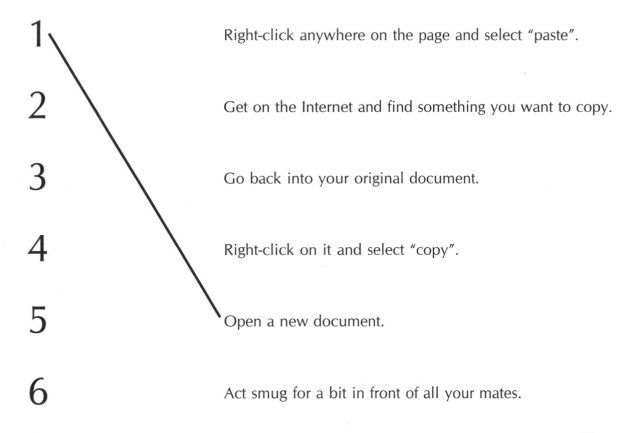

1   Right-click anywhere on the page and select "paste".

2   Get on the Internet and find something you want to copy.

3   Go back into your original document.

4   Right-click on it and select "copy".

5   Open a new document.

6   Act smug for a bit in front of all your mates.

Make a list of the world's funniest jokes...

Find a joke on the Internet — it could be a really good joke or a joke that makes everybody groan. Then copy and paste this joke into a word processor document — but don't tell anybody your joke. When everybody in the class has pasted their joke into this document, read all the jokes and vote for the one you think is the best.

Here's a funny joke to start your list off:
Q: My dog is a nuisance — he chases everyone on a bicycle — what can I do?   A: Take his bike away.

Unit 6D — Using the Internet for Research

Copyright

There are proper laws about what you can and can't copy... They're pretty boring. Sorry.

Copyright is Darned Annoying

Even though you can copy and paste things off the Internet, you have to be careful because —

 **YOU'RE NOT ALWAYS ALLOWED TO**.

Basically, when someone has the **copyright** for a certain thing (this can be a picture, a book, a piece of text or even an entire website) **it means they own it**.

> This means they have **control** over how it can be used.
> If you use something that's owned by someone else without them
> knowing, it's like **stealing** and you can get in a lot of trouble.

Ask before you use Other People's Ideas

If you want to use something from someone else's website, you have to ask for permission — but this can take ages.

> It can also be really irritating if the owners often try to make you use their stuff in the way that THEY want, not the way that YOU want.

Okay, you can use our ice cream, but you're not allowed to enjoy it.

> e.g. I asked Mr Freeze the ice-cream man if I could use his logo.
> He told me I couldn't say anything that made him look bad. I ended up not
> using the logo because I wanted to say that Mr Freeze made me vomit.

Always say Where you got Information from

There is a way round this (sort of) — **make sure you say where you got your information from**.

For example:

- Let's say I really want some facts about Australian Television Actors, but all the information on their website is **copyrighted**.

Oi — you haven't got the copyright on those sausages you mongrel...

- I can still use some of the information in my project, but only if I make sure everyone knows where I found it out.

- It's kind of like stealing someone's idea, but making sure everyone knows who you pinched it off — then (for some weird reason) everyone's happy.

- So, it's pretty important to remember **WHERE** you found stuff out, so you can avoid stealing...

Unit 6D — Using the Internet for Research

Copyright

① Fill in the gaps with the right words.

tickle

control

china

When someone has the ....

for something (e.g. a book), it means

copy

eaten

that they .... who can

.... it and how it gets ....

used

copyright

throw

② If you use copyrighted information or pictures without permission, what are you doing?

☐ Borrowing

☐ Having a laugh

☐ Stealing

☐ Juggling

I suppose you think this is some sort of a joke?

③ What's it important to say when you use any information?

....

 **Computer Activity**

Making a Page

For this project you will need: access to the Internet and a word processor.

In this project you will:

Research and make your own newspaper article

Pick a topic

 Pick a topic that you want to tell other people about. You're going to find out as much as you can about it, then write it up in a computer document.

 Think about who will read your article.
- How old are they?
- How much will they know already?
- What kind of things do you want to tell them?

Research your topic

 Think of different places where you can find information.

— Books
— Newspapers and Magazines
— CD-ROMs
— The Internet

> Or use any other source of information you can think of.

Use a search engine on the Internet to help find information.

- Remember to think carefully about the words you type in to search for. Use AND to help narrow down your results.

- Make a list of where you got all your information from, so that you don't break copyright laws. <u>You'll need to write this list at the end of your article.</u>

Think carefully about the information you've found

Think hard about the information you've found.

Does all of it agree, or do some things contradict each other?

 Check for bias and ask yourself these questions:

— Who wrote it?
— What is it saying?
— Could there be another side to the story?
— What can I compare it with?

Unit 6D — Using the Internet for Research